Glencoe
McGraw-Hill

New York, New York   Columbus, Ohio   Woodland Hills, California   Peoria, Illinois

To the Teacher

These pages provide a synopsis of the chapter by section, including suggested discussion questions. Also included are the terms that fill in the blanks in the students' *Note-taking Worksheets* that are found in the Chapter Resources booklets. Chapter vocabulary terms appear in bold within the outlines, both in the teacher and student versions.

Glencoe/McGraw-Hill

A Division of The McGraw-Hill Companies

Send all inquiries to:

Glencoe/McGraw-Hill
8787 Orion Place
Columbus, OH 43240

ISBN 0-07-826887-7

Printed in the United States of America

1 2 3 4 5 6 7 8 9 10 047 06 05 04 03 02 01

Table of Contents

Content Outline for Teaching # Table of Contents

The Nature of Science

Underlined words and phrases are to be filled in by students on the Note-taking Worksheet.

Section 1   What is science?

A. <u>Science</u>—a way of learning about the natural world

   1. Scientists ask <u>questions</u> about the natural world, but questions about art, politics, personal preferences, or morality can't be answered by science.

   2. Answers are <u>uncertain</u> because new knowledge and discoveries are continually being made.

   3. **Scientific <u>theory</u>**—an attempted explanation for repeatedly observed patterns in the natural world

   4. A rule that describes a pattern in nature is a **scientific <u>law</u>.**

B. Scientists study <u>systems</u>—collections of structures, cycles, and processes that relate to and interact with each other.

C. Science is divided into <u>three</u> main branches that study different systems.

   1. <u>Life</u> **science** studies living things and how they interact.

   2. Earth and space systems are studied in **<u>Earth</u> science.**

   3. <u>Physical</u> **science** studies matter and energy.

   4. The practical use of science is called **<u>technology</u>.**

Discussion Question

What is the difference between a scientific theory and a scientific law? A scientific theory explains, and a scientific law describes.

END

The Nature of Science

Underlined words and phrases are to be filled in by students on the Note-taking Worksheet.

Section 2   Science in Action

A. The <u>scientific method</u> includes observing, questioning, and researching; forming an **hypothesis**; predicting an outcome; investigating; analyzing; forming conclusions, communicating findings; and repeating the process.

B. Scientists **infer** conclusions based on observations.

C. A **controlled experiment** is one type of scientific investigation.
   1. Factors that can be changed in an experiment are **variables.**
   2. **Constants** are variables that remain unchanged.

D. <u>Safety</u> is important for both laboratory and field scientists

Discussion Question

What does a scientist use to infer a conclusion? observations

END

CHAPTER 1 — Content Outline for Teaching

The Nature of Science

Underlined words and phrases are to be filled in by students on the Note-taking Worksheet.

Section 3   Models in Science

A. <u>Model</u>—representation of an object or event used as a tool for understanding the natural world

B. Models come in <u>three</u> basic types.
   1. <u>Physical</u> models can be seen and touched.
   2. <u>Computer</u> models can be seen on a computer screen but not touched.
   3. <u>Idea</u> models are concepts that describe how someone thinks about something in the natural world.

C. Models have several <u>uses</u>.
   1. Models <u>communicate</u> observations and ideas.
   2. Models can <u>test</u> predictions.
   3. Models can <u>save</u> time, money, and lives.

D. Models <u>change</u> over time as new observations and discoveries are made.

Discussion Question

What are the purposes of models? to communicate, to test predictions, and to save time, money, and lives

The Nature of Science

Underlined words and phrases are to be filled in by students on the Note-taking Worksheet.

Section 4   Evaluating Scientific Explanation

A. <u>Critical thinking</u>—using what is known to decide if new facts should be agreed with or believed

B. <u>Data</u> should be evaluated.
   1. The data should be <u>specific</u> and exact.
   2. Observations should be carefully, accurately, and completely <u>noted</u>.
   3. Data must be <u>repeatable</u> to be reliable.

C. <u>Conclusions</u> should be evaluated.
   1. Conclusions should <u>make sense</u>.
   2. <u>Other explanations</u> should be considered before a single conclusion is reached.

D. <u>Advertising</u> claims should be carefully analyzed since they are designed to sell products rather than to promote scientific evidence impartially.

Discussion Question

What aspects of a scientific explanation should be carefully evaluated?
the data and conclusions

END

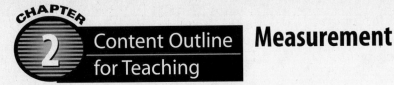
Underlined words and phrases are to be filled in by students on the Note-taking Worksheet.

Section 1   Description and Measurement

A. <u>Measurement</u>—describes world using numbers
   1. Types of measurement—distance, time, <u>speed</u>, volume, mass
   2. Measurement can also help describe <u>events</u>.

B. Approximated measurement based on previous experience is **estimation**.
   1. Estimation is useful when actual measurements are <u>not easily</u> made.
   2. Estimation can check that an answer is <u>reasonable</u>.
   3. When you estimate, you often use the word <u>about</u>.

C. Precision and accuracy
   1. <u>Precision</u>—a description of how close measurements are to each other
      a. Used to discuss number of <u>decimal places</u> a measuring device can measure
      b. Degree of Precision—today's measuring devices are more <u>precise</u>.
   2. <u>Accuracy</u>—comparison of measurement to actual value
   3. Precision and accuracy are important in many <u>medical</u> procedures.
   4. Measurements can be <u>rounded</u> when precision is not needed.
   5. <u>Significant digits</u>—reflect true precision of a calculation
      a. Multiplication or division—measurement with the <u>fewest</u> digits determines the number of significant digits.
      b. Addition or subtraction—significance determined to the place value of the <u>least</u> precise measurement

Discussion Question

How can estimation be useful? when actual measurements are too difficult to obtain; when verifying realism of a calculation

END

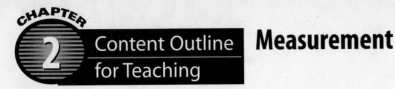

CHAPTER 2

Content Outline for Teaching

Measurement

Underlined words and phrases are to be filled in by students on the Note-taking Worksheet.

Section 2   SI Units

A. The International System—**SI** units, in multiples of <u>ten</u>, provide a standard of consistent measurement for global science, business, and industry.

B. Length—the distance between two points; SI unit—**meter**
   1. Measure pencil—use <u>centimeters</u>
   2. Measure distance from New York to Chicago—use <u>kilometers</u>

C. <u>Volume</u>—amount of space an object takes up; SI unit—<u>cubic meter</u>
   1. To find volume of regular shape—measure length, width, and <u>height</u> and multiply
   2. To find volume of irregular shape—volume by <u>immersion</u>

D. **Mass**—amount of matter in an object; SI unit—**kilogram**

E. Weight—measurement of force; SI unit—<u>newton</u>

F. Temperature—measure of kinetic energy in particles of matter; SI unit—**kelvin**

G. Time—interval between two events; SI unit—<u>second</u>

H. <u>Rate</u>—amount of change of one measurement in a given amount of time

Discussion Question

Why is it important to have one international system of measurement? to avoid confusion

END

E. A **transformer** changes the voltage of an alternating current.

   1. Using two <u>coils</u> of wire wrapped around an <u>iron</u> core produces an <u>input</u> voltage and an <u>output</u> voltage.

   2. The ratio of coils on the input side of a transformer to coils on the output side is <u>the same as</u> the ratio of the input voltage to the output voltage.

F. The <u>connection</u> between magnetism and electricity is illustrated by an <u>electric</u> guitar.

   1. Small magnets produce a <u>magnetic field</u> around the strings.

   2. The magnetic <u>domains</u> in the strings line up, producing another magnetic field.

   3. When strummed, the strings vibrate, changing the surrounding <u>magnetic</u> field, causing changes in the coil to vibrate.

   4. The motion of the charges is an <u>electric current</u> that can be amplified and sent through speakers to create sound.

Discussion Question

What is the difference between direct current (DC) and alternating current (AC)? Direct current flows in one direction; alternating current changes direction—positive and negative—many times per second

END

Underlined words and phrases are to be filled in by students on the Note-taking Worksheet.

Section 3   Drawings, Tables, and Graphs

A. <u>Scientific</u> Illustrations—often make information more clear than written text can
   1. <u>Drawings</u>—can emphasize only necessary details or show things you can't see
   2. <u>Photographs</u>—show an object exactly as it is at a single moment

B. <u>Tables</u>—display information in rows and columns for easier comprehension

C. <u>Graphs</u>—collect, organize, and summarize data visually
   1. **<u>Line graph</u>**—shows relationship between two variables, which must be <u>numbers</u>
   2. **<u>Bar graph</u>**—uses bars of different sizes to show relationships between variables; one variable is divided into parts; the other variable is a number
   3. **<u>Circle graph</u>**—shows parts of a whole as percentages
   4. <u>Scales</u> on graphs must be carefully constructed and analyzed so users easily understand the information.

Discussion Question

How are graphs useful? They visually present data in an easy to understand way.

END

Underlined words and phrases are to be filled in by students on the Note-taking Worksheet.

Section 2   Electricity and Magnetism

A. An **electromagnet** is a current-carrying wire wrapped around an iron core.

   1. The <u>magnetic field</u> of an electromagnet is turned on or off when the electric current is turned on or off.

   2. <u>Doorbells</u> and high-speed trains use electromagnets to operate.

B. Current-carrying <u>wires</u> produce a magnetic field that acts the same way as a magnet's magnetic field.

   1. Two current-carrying wires can attract or repel each other as if they were two <u>magnets</u>.

   2. The magnetic field around a wire causes it to be <u>pushed</u> or <u>pulled</u> by a magnet, depending on the direction the current is flowing in the wire.

   3. An **electric motor** (device that converts electrical energy into kinetic energy) runs by using the magnetic field formed by a <u>current-carrying wire</u> formed into a loop.

C. Charged particles from the Sun follow Earth's magnetic field to the poles where they create the **aurora**.

D. A **generator** uses a magnetic field to turn motion into electricity.

   1. An **alternating current** (AC) changes from positive to negative due to a looped wire changing direction of motion.

   2. A generator can produce both <u>direct current</u> (DC), which flows in one direction, and AC current; large power plants produce <u>AC current</u>.

   3. <u>Energy sources</u> such as gas, coal, and water provide power plants with kinetic energy to generate electricity.

   4. <u>Voltage</u> is a measure of how much energy electric charges in a current are carrying.

TURN

Atoms, Elements, and the Periodic Table

Section 1 Structure of Matter

A. **Matter**—anything that has <u>mass</u> and takes up space

  1. The **atom**—a small particle that makes up most types of <u>matter</u>

  2. Lavoisier introduced the **law of conservation of matter**—matter is neither <u>created</u> nor <u>destroyed</u>, but only changes form.

  3. Before Lavoisier, people used to think <u>matter</u> could appear and disappear.

  4. Dalton introduced an early atomic <u>theory of matter</u>.

    a. <u>Atoms</u> are too small to be seen by human eye.

    b. Each type of matter is made of <u>only one kind</u> of atom.

  5. Thomson discovered that atoms are made of even smaller <u>subatomic particles</u>.

    a. **Electrons**—tiny, negatively charged particles with mass

    b. Proposed that an atom was a ball of <u>positive charge</u> with electrons embedded in it

  6. <u>Rutherford</u> suggested a new model of the atom.

    a. **Nucleus**—the positively charged central part of the atom

    b. **Protons**—the <u>positively</u> charged particles in the nucleus

    c. Electrons are scattered in the mostly empty space around the <u>nucleus</u>

  7. Chadwick introduced **neutrons**—particles that come from the nucleus and have no charge.

  8. <u>Electron Cloud</u> Model — Electrons are so small and fast that they move in a cloud.

Discussion Question

According to the law of conservation of matter, what happens to wood when it "burns up"? Matter is neither created nor destroyed, but only changes form. Wood and the oxygen from the air that it combines with during burning have the same mass as the ash, water, and carbon dioxide produced.

END

> Underlined words and phrases are to be filled in by students on the Note-taking Worksheet.

Section 1   What is magnetism?

A. Thousands of years ago people discovered <u>magnetite</u>.

   1. Iron acted like magnetite when <u>rubbed</u> with it.

   2. Pieces would point <u>north</u> when allowed to turn.

B. Magnets have a north and south pole; north and south poles <u>attract</u> each other, while two norths or two souths <u>repel</u> each other.

   1. **Magnetic field**—the area around a magnet through which the magnetic force is exerted

     a. Magnetic field lines begin at a <u>north</u> pole and end at a <u>south</u> pole.

     b. The magnetic field is strongest close to the <u>poles</u>.

   2. Moving <u>electric charges</u> produce a magnetic field.

     a. A group of atoms with their fields pointing in the same direction is called a <u>magnetic domain</u>.

     b. A magnet contains a <u>large</u> number of magnetic domains.

C. Earth's magnetic field, the **magnetosphere**, extends into space and originates in the molten iron outer core.

   1. Some <u>animals</u>, such as homing pigeons, have magnetite in their brains that helps them navigate.

   2. Earth's magnetic field <u>changes</u> over time.

     a. It has even <u>reversed</u>.

     b. Ancient <u>rocks</u> reveal magnetic field <u>orientation</u> from long ago.

   3. A <u>compass</u>, a magnetic needle free to turn, can be used to detect Earth's magnetic field.

Discussion Question

Where does Earth's magnetosphere originate? In the molten iron of the outer core

END

Atoms, Elements, and the Periodic Table

Underlined words and phrases are to be filled in by students on the Note-taking Worksheet.

Section 2   The Simplest Matter

A. **Elements**—matter made up of <u>only one</u> kind of atom
   1. There are <u>115</u> known elements.
   2. 90 <u>naturally</u> occurring elements, 25 <u>synthetic</u> elements—made by scientists

B. Periodic Table—Chart that organizes and displays information about the <u>elements</u>
   1. **Atomic <u>number</u>**—the top number in the element's periodic table block
      a. Tells the number of <u>protons</u> in the nucleus of each atom of that element
      b. The number of <u>protons</u> remains constant in every atom of an element.
   2. <u>**Isotopes**</u>—atoms of the same element that have different numbers of <u>neutrons</u>
   3. **Mass number**—number of <u>protons</u> plus number of <u>neutrons</u>
   4. **Atomic <u>mass</u>**—the number found below the element symbol
      a. The average <u>mass</u> of an atom of an element
      b. The unit used for atomic mass is the <u>atomic mass unit</u>, which is given the symbol u.

C. Elements fall into three general groups characterized by similar <u>properties</u>
   1. <u>**Metals**</u>—most of the elements
      a. <u>Shiny</u> luster
      b. Good conductors of <u>heat</u> and <u>electricity</u>
      c. Most are <u>solids</u> at room temperature.
      d. <u>Malleable</u>, or can be shaped
      e. <u>Ductile</u>, or can be drawn into wires without breaking
   2. <u>**Nonmetals**</u>—found on the right side of the periodic table
      a. <u>Dull</u> in appearance
      b. <u>Poor</u> conductors of heat and electricity
      c. Many are <u>gases</u> at room temperature.
      d. <u>Brittle</u>, cannot change shape without breaking
      e. 96 percent of the <u>human body</u> is made up of nonmetals.

TURN

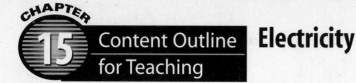

CHAPTER 15 Content Outline for Teaching   Electricity

> Underlined words and phrases are to be filled in by students on the Note-taking Worksheet.

Section 3   Electric Circuits

A. The amount of current is determined by the <u>voltage</u> supplied by a battery and the resistance of the conductor.

   1. As the resistance in an electric current increases, the current in the circuit <u>decreases</u>.

   2. <u>**Ohm's law**</u>—current = voltage/resistance

   3. When the voltage in a circuit increases, the <u>current</u> increases.

B. There are <u>two</u> kinds of basic circuits: series and parallel.

   1. A <u>**series**</u> circuit has only one path for the electric current to follow—if path is broken, the current will no longer flow and all devices in the circuit stop working.

   2. A <u>**parallel**</u> circuit has more than one path for the electric current to follow.

C. For safety, circuits in homes and buildings have <u>fuses</u> or circuit breakers that limit the amount of current in the wiring.

D. <u>**Electric power**</u>—rate at which an appliance converts electrical energy to another form of energy

   1. Power = current × voltage

   2. The unit of power is the <u>watt</u>.

   3. Electric companies charge customers for the number of <u>kilowatt-hours</u> they use in a month.

E. Electricity can be <u>dangerous</u>.

   1. Current can enter your body and shock you when your body accidentally becomes part of an electric circuit.

   2. Lightning can be deadly; if caught outdoors near lightning use a lightning-safety position—squat on the balls of the feet with hands on knees.

Discussion Question

How does the body receive an electric shock? The body becomes part of an electric circuit; ions in the body conduct charge.

END

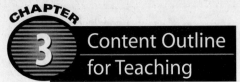

Content Outline for Teaching

3. <u>Metalloids</u>—found between the metals and nonmetals on the periodic table
   a. Have characteristics of both <u>metals</u> and <u>nonmetals</u>
   b. Do not <u>conduct</u> heat and electricity as well as metals
   c. All are <u>solids</u> at room temperature.

Discussion Question

What do you know about chlorine, based only on the fact that it is a non-metal? It is probably a gas at room temperature. It probably does not conduct heat and electricity very well. It is probably dull in appearance. It cannot change shape without breaking.

END

Section 2   Electric Current

A. <u>Electric current</u>—flow of charge through a conductor

   1. In solids the flowing charges are <u>electrons</u>; in liquids the flowing charges are positive or negative ions.

      a. <u>Circuit</u>—closed conducting loop through which electric currents continuously flow

      b. Current <u>flow</u> can do work in an electric device; flow carries electrical energy through wire.

      c. <u>Voltage</u>—measure of how much electric energy a battery can provide

      d. Electrons move in a circuit and have millions and millions of <u>collisions</u>.

   2. The voltage of a battery depends on the amount and type of <u>chemicals</u> used to create the chemical reactions in a battery.

   3. Batteries <u>die</u> when the original chemicals are used up and the chemical reactions in the battery stop.

B. <u>Resistance</u>—measure of how difficult it is for electrons to flow through a material

   1. Insulators generally have much <u>higher</u> resistance then conductors.

   2. The amount of electric energy that is converted into thermal energy <u>increases</u> as the resistance of wire increases.

   3. The length and <u>diameter</u> of a wire affect electron flow.

Discussion Question

Why do batteries die? The chemicals providing the source of chemical reactions are used up.

END

Atoms, Elements, and the Periodic Table

Section 3 Compounds and Mixtures

A. Substance—Matter that has the same <u>composition</u> and properties throughout

B. Compound—Substance whose smallest unit is made up of atoms of <u>more than one</u> element

   1. <u>Chemical formula</u>—tells which elements make up a compound as well as how many atoms of each element are present

      a. The subscript number tells <u>how many atoms</u> of the preceding element are in the compound.

      b. No subscript is used when <u>only one atom</u> of the element is present.

   2. A given compound is always made of the same elements in the same <u>proportion</u>.

C. Mixture—two or more substances mixed together which don't make a <u>new</u> substance

   1. Unlike in compounds, the <u>proportions</u> of the substances in a mixture can be changed without changing the identity of the mixture.

   2. Examples: air, <u>blood</u>

   3. Can <u>separate</u> mixtures easily

   4. <u>Homogenous</u> mixtures—the same throughout

   5. <u>Heterogenous</u> mixtures—you can see the different parts

Discussion Question

What is the difference between compounds and mixtures? Compounds are single substances; mixtures are two or more substances mixed together. Compounds always contain the same elements in the same proportion; the proportions of the substances in a mixture can be changed. Mixtures can be easily separated; compounds cannot.

END

Electricity

Section 1   Electric Charge

A. Electricity begins at the <u>atomic</u> level where protons and electrons have electric charge.

    1. <u>**Protons**</u> carry a positive change.

    2. Electrons carry a <u>negative</u> charge.

    3. <u>**Ions**</u> form when atoms lose or gain electrons and become positively or negatively charged.

    4. Electrons can move from object to object; <u>static charge</u> is the buildup of electric charge on an object.

    5. A flow of charge can be caused by ions moving in a <u>solution</u>.

B. All objects exert an <u>**electric force**</u> on each other; it can be attractive or repulsive.

    1. Like charges repel, unlike charges <u>attract</u>.

    2. Electric charges exert a force on each other at a distance through an <u>**electric field**</u> which exists around every electric charge

C. <u>**Insulator**</u>—material which does not allow electrons to move easily; <u>**conductor**</u>—material that allows electrons to move easily; metals are the best conductors

D. <u>**Electric discharge**</u>—rapid movement of excess charge from one place to another; lightning is an electric discharge.

E. <u>Grounding</u>—provides a pathway to drain excess charge into the Earth; lightning rods provide grounding for many buildings.

Discussion Question

What is static charge? Buildup of electric charge on an object

END

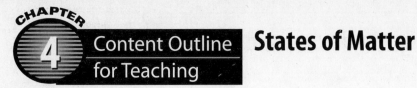

States of Matter

Underlined words and phrases are to be filled in by students on the Note-taking Worksheet.

Section 1   Matter

A. <u>Matter</u>—anything that takes up space and has mass; matter is composed of tiny particles.

   1. Three usual <u>states of matter</u> are solid, liquid, and gas.

   2. <u>Plasma,</u> a fourth state, occurs only at very high temperatures and is not common on Earth.

B. <u>Solids</u>—have definite shape and volume because particles are packed closely together and merely vibrate in place.

   1. Solids in which particles are arranged in a repeating, three-dimensional pattern are called <u>crystals</u> or crystalline solids.

   2. <u>Amorphous</u> solids have a random arrangement of particles.

C. Matter with a definite volume but no definite shape is a <u>**liquid**</u>; a liquid's particles move more freely than those of a solid.

   1. <u>Viscosity</u> is a liquid's resistance to flow and increases when particles are more strongly attracted to each other.

   2. <u>Surface tension</u>—uneven forces acting on the particles of a liquid's surface.

D. <u>Gas</u>—matter that does not have a definite shape or volume; gas particles spread out evenly as far apart as possible.

Discussion Question

Why do some liquids have greater viscosity than others do? Liquids with greater viscosity have particles more strongly attracted to each other than do liquids with less viscosity.

END

CHAPTER 14 Content Outline for Teaching

Light, Mirrors, and Lenses

Underlined words and phrases are to be filled in by students on the Note-taking Worksheet.

Section 4   Using Mirrors and Lenses

A. Compound <u>microscope</u>—uses two convex lenses, the objective lens and the eye-piece lens, to magnify an image

B. A key difference between a telescope and a microscope is the <u>size</u> of the objective lens; a telescope uses a large lens to gather light from distant objects.

   1. <u>**Refracting**</u> **telescope**—uses two convex lenses, an objective lens and an eye-piece, to form an image of a distant object

   2. <u>**Reflecting**</u> **telescopes** use a <u>concave</u> mirror to focus light onto a secondary mirror that directs the image to the eyepiece.

C. A <u>camera</u> uses a convex lens to form an inverted image on light-sensitive film.

D. Unlike ordinary light, a <u>laser</u> beam doesn't spread out as it travels.

   1. A beam of light produced by an ordinary flashlight spreads out as it travels.

   2. In a beam of laser light, the crests and troughs of the light waves <u>overlap</u> so the waves are in phase.

      a. Large amounts of energy can be applied to a very <u>small</u> area.

      b. Can replace <u>scalpels</u> in surgery

Discussion Question

What is a key difference between the purposes of convex lenses in microscopes and telescopes? The convex lenses in microscopes magnify an image of a small object; the convex lenses in a telescope gather light from distant objects so they can be viewed.

END

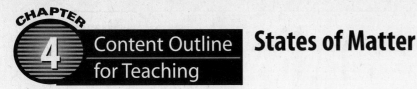

States of Matter

Underlined words and phrases are to be filled in by students on the Note-taking Worksheet.

Section 2 — Changes of State

A. Particles are in constant motion; amount of movement depends on their <u>kinetic energy</u>.

   1. <u>Thermal energy</u>—total energy of all the particles in a sample of matter

   2. The average kinetic energy of particles in a substance is its **temperature.**

   3. <u>Heat</u>—movement of thermal energy from a substance with a higher temperature to one with a lower temperature

B. <u>Specific heat</u>—amount of heat needed to raise the temperature of 1 g of a substance 1°C

C. Matter can <u>change</u> states as energy is absorbed or released.

   1. A change from the solid to the liquid state is called **melting**.

   2. A change from the liquid to the solid state is called **freezing**.

D. Changes between **liquid and gas** states

   1. A change from liquid to gas is called **vaporization**.

      a. <u>Boiling</u> is vaporization which occurs below the liquid's surface at its boiling point.

      b. <u>Evaporation</u> is vaporization which occurs at the surface of a liquid; molecules must be at or near the surface at the right speed to evaporate.

   2. **Condensation**—a change from gas to liquid

E. Changes between solid and gas states—During <u>sublimation</u> the surface particles of a solid gain enough energy to become a gas.

Discussion Question

How do heat and specific heat differ? Heat is a movement of thermal energy; specific heat is the amount of heat needed to increase the temperature of 1 g of a substance by 1°C.

END

Light, Mirrors, and Lenses

Underlined words and phrases are to be filled in by students on the Note-taking Worksheet.

Section 3   Refraction and Lenses

A. Refraction
1. The speed of light
   a. The speed of light in <u>empty space</u> is about 300,000,000 m/s.
   b. Light travels <u>more slowly</u> when it travels through material such as air, water, or glass.
2. The bending of light waves caused by a change in speed as they pass through different media is called <u>refraction</u>.

B. <u>Lens</u>—transparent object with at least one curved side that causes light to bend
1. <u>Convex</u> lens—thicker in the center than at the edges; forms an image based on how far the object is from the focal point
2. A <u>concave</u> lens—thicker at the edges than at the middle; causes light rays to diverge forming an upright image smaller than the actual object

C. Total internal reflection occurs when <u>all</u> the light waves that strike the boundary between two transparent materials can be reflected.
1. At the <u>critical angle</u> all the light is reflected.
2. The <u>size</u> of the critical angle depends on the two materials involved.

D. Optical fibers
1. Can make a <u>light beam</u> travel in a path that is curved or twisted
2. All the light that enters one end of the fiber comes out the other end because of <u>total internal reflection</u>.
3. A thin fiber of glass or plastic, covered with another material called <u>cladding</u>
4. Used in <u>communications</u>

Discussion Question

What is refraction? the bending of light waves as they change speed when passing through different media

END

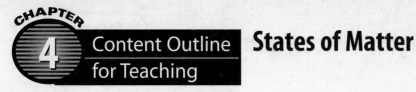

States of Matter

Section 3   Behavior of Fluids

A. <u>Pressure</u> equals the force exerted on a surface divided by the total area over which the force is exerted or, $P = F / A$.

   1. If force <u>increases</u> over an area, the pressure increases; if force over an area <u>decreases</u>, the pressure decreases.

   2. <u>Atmospheric pressure</u>—air presses down on Earth with force.

   3. Pressure can be <u>balanced</u> as the pressure pushing down equals the pressure pushing up.

   4. As <u>altitude</u> increases, air pressure decreases.

B. Gas pressure in a closed container <u>changes</u> with volume and temperature changes.

   1. Decreasing volume <u>increases</u> pressure; increasing volume <u>decreases</u> pressure.

   2. Increasing temperature <u>increases</u> pressure; decreasing temperature <u>decreases</u> pressure.

C. <u>Buoyant force</u>—an upward force on an object immersed in a fluid

   1. <u>Archimedes' principle</u>—Buoyant force on an object is equal to the weight of the fluid displaced by the object.

   2. <u>Density</u> is mass divided by volume.

   a. An object will <u>float</u> in a fluid that is denser than the object.

   b. An object with the same density as the fluid will stay at the <u>same</u> level in the fluid.

   c. An object will <u>sink</u> in a fluid that is less dense that the object.

D. <u>Pascal's principle</u>—When a force is applied to a confined fluid, an increase in pressure is transmitted equally to all parts of the fluid.

   1. <u>Hydraulic systems</u> allow people to lift heavy objects with relatively little force.

   2. When squeezed, liquids will be pushed out of a <u>force pump</u>, a closed container with a hole in it.

Discussion Question

Why does air pressure decrease with altitude? At higher altitudes air particles can spread out farther from each other, reducing pressure.

Content Outline for Teaching

Light, Mirrors, and Lenses

Underlined words and phrases are to be filled in by students on the Note-taking Worksheet.

Section 2   Reflection and Mirrors

A. The **law of** <u>reflection</u> says that the angle of incidence is equal to the angle of reflection.

   1. The uneven reflection of light waves from a rough surface is called <u>diffuse</u> reflection.

   2. <u>Regular</u> reflection results from a smooth surface such as a mirror.

   3. <u>Scattering</u>—light waves traveling in one direction are made to travel in many different directions.

   4. Plane mirror—reflects an actual size image that seems to be behind the mirror due to the way the <u>brain</u> interprets light

B. Concave mirrors cause light rays to <u>converge</u>; convex mirrors cause light rays to <u>diverge</u>.

   1. In a concave mirror, light waves parallel to the optical axis reflect and pass through the **focal point**.

     a. Focal length—distance along the optical axis from the center of the mirror to the <u>focal point</u>

     b. The image formed by a concave mirror depends on the <u>position</u> of an object relative to the focal point.

     c. Flashlights and headlights form a <u>beam</u> of light when a light source is placed at the mirror's focal point.

   2. The image formed by a convex mirror is <u>upright</u> and <u>smaller</u> than the actual object; convex mirrors are used for security in stores and on vehicle outside rearview mirrors.

Discussion Question

What is diffuse reflection? the uneven reflection of light waves from a rough surface

END

Properties and Changes of Matter

Section 1   Physical Properties

A. Physical property—any characteristic of matter that can be observed without changing the identity of the material

   1. Physical properties include color, shape, smell, taste, <u>mass</u>, <u>volume</u>, and density.

   2. **Density**—amount of mass in a given volume; a golf ball would have greater density than a table-tennis ball; the formula for density is: density (g/cm^3) = mass (g)/volume (cm^3)

   3. Density can be used to <u>identify</u> unknown substances; a person could determine the composition of a piece of jewelry by comparing its density with the density of a known substance such as silver or gold.

   4. **State of matter**—whether a substance is a solid, liquid, or a gas at a particular temperature and pressure

   5. Some physical properties are size-<u>dependent</u> (length, width, height, volume, and mass) while others are size-<u>independent</u> (density, color, state).

B. Matter can be <u>classified</u> as an acid or a base.

   1. <u>Acids</u> tend to have a sharp smell and a sour taste (but you should NEVER taste anything in a laboratory) with a pH between 0 and 7; citrus fruits contain acids.

   2. <u>Bases</u> feel slippery and taste bitter and have a pH of between 7 and 14; a bar of soap is a base.

   3. Water, with a pH of exactly <u>7</u>, is neither an acid nor a base; it is neutral.

Discussion Question

What are some physical properties? Color, shape, smell, taste, mass, volume, density, state, and acid/base classification

END

Light, Mirrors, and Lenses

Underlined words and phrases are to be filled in by students on the Note-taking Worksheet.

Section 1 Properties of Light

A. Light is a wave that carries energy; a light source emits a countless number of **light rays** that travel in all directions.

   1. The material through which a wave travels is called a **medium**.

   2. Light is an electromagnetic wave that does not need a medium in which to travel.

B. For the eyes to see an object, light must strike the object and bounce off, a process called **reflection**.

   1. Materials that let no light pass through them are opaque.

   2. Transparent materials let almost all light pass through them.

   3. Materials that let some, but not all, light pass through are translucent.

C. White light is composed of different wavelengths, which have colors ranging from red to violet.

   1. Objects appear to have color because they absorb some light waves and reflect others; an object appears the color of the light it reflects.

   2. All visible colors can be made by mixing light from the three primary colors of red, blue, and green.

   3. Mixing pigment to form colors is different than mixing light to form colors; the primary pigment colors are yellow, magenta, and cyan.

Discussion Question

How do the eyes see an object? The eyes see an object when the object reflects light into the eyes.

END

Properties and Changes of Matter

Section 2 Chemical Properties

A. <u>Chemical property</u>—characteristic of something that allows it to change to something new

   1. Chemical properties include flammability, toxicity, and **<u>reactivity</u>** with oxygen; when a half-eaten apple turns brown in the air, a chemical reaction with oxygen has occurred.

   2. Silver and gold have lower reactivity than many other metals, which helps make them good choices for <u>jewelry</u>.

   3. Chlorine compounds change the chemical properties of <u>pool</u> water, making it more acidic in order to eliminate algae, bacteria, and insects.

     a. Standing water, without added chlorine, can become a breeding ground for insects, such as **<u>mosquitoes</u>**.

     b. Plants, <u>algae</u>, and bacteria can make a pool unfit for swimming.

     c. The more acidic chlorinated pool water can also irritate the skin and <u>eyes</u> of swimmers.

B. Acids and bases have chemical properties that make them both <u>useful</u> and <u>harmful</u>.

   1. Many acids react with, or <u>corrode</u>, certain metals and can harm living organisms.

     a. Tomato sauce is acidic enough to react with <u>aluminum</u> foil, but will not harm human beings.

     b. Acid rain can damage plant and animal <u>tissues</u>.

     c. <u>Sulphuric</u> acid is useful in industry, but causes burns on skin.

   2. Strong bases can <u>damage</u> living tissue; ammonia fumes can cause nosebleeds in some people.

   3. <u>Salts</u>—compounds made of a metal and nonmetal and that are formed when acids and bases react

     a. <u>Table</u> salt can be formed from a base sodium hydroxide and hydrochloric acid.

     b. Calcium carbonate, or <u>chalk</u>, and ammonium chloride, which is used in batteries, are useful salts.

Discussion Question

What are three chemical properties? Flammability, toxicity, and reactivity with oxygen

END

CHAPTER 13 Content Outline for Teaching | **Electromagnetic Waves**

> Underlined words and phrases are to be filled in by students on the Note-taking Worksheet.

Section 3 Using Electromagnetic Waves

A. The world is becoming increasingly connected through the use of electromagnetic waves in <u>telecommunication</u>.

B. <u>Radio</u> waves are the electromagnetic wave of choice for most telecommunication technology.

   1. The assigned frequency for a TV or radio station signal wave is its **carrier wave**.

   2. In <u>amplitude modulation</u>, the amplitude of the carrier wave is changed to transmit information; the frequency is not changed.

   3. In <u>frequency modulation</u>, the frequency of the carrier wave is changed.

C. <u>Telephones</u> can convert sound waves to an electrical signal that can be converted to radio waves, microwaves, or light waves. Receivers convert the transmission back into an electric signal, and a speaker changes the electric signal into a <u>sound</u> wave.

   1. <u>Cordless</u> phones and <u>cellular</u> phones use radio waves to transmit signals.

   2. <u>Pagers</u> use electromagnetic signals from a base station.

D. Communication <u>satellites</u> enable radio signals to be sent from one part of Earth to another.

E. The **Global Positioning System** consists of satellites, ground-based stations, and portable units with receivers used to help locate objects on Earth.

Discussion Question

What is the most versatile electromagnetic wave to use for telecommunication? radio waves

END

Properties and Changes of Matter

Section 3   Physical and Chemical Changes

A. <u>Physical change</u>—any change in size, shape, form, or state where the identity of the matter stays the same

   1. Cutting a watermelon into slices is an example of a <u>physical</u> change.

   2. Change of <u>state</u> is a common physical change.
     a. Solid to <u>liquid</u> (ice melting)
     b. <u>Liquid</u> to solid (water freezing)
     c. Liquid to <u>gas</u> (water boiling and creating steam)
     d. <u>Gas</u> to liquid (water vapor condensing into water such as when dew forms)

B. <u>Chemical change</u>—one material changes into a different material with different properties or characteristics

   1. <u>Examples</u> of chemical changes include digestion, photosynthesis, paint drying, and oil burning.

   2. In a chemical change, <u>new</u> materials are formed that are different from the starting materials.

   3. A chemical change cannot easily be <u>reversed</u>.

   4. Signs of chemical changes include the release or absorption of <u>energy</u> in the form of light, heat, or sound; formation of a gas or solid, not from a change of state, can indicate a chemical change.

C. Leaves changing color indicates a chemical change in <u>nature</u>.

   1. <u>Weathering</u> of the Earth's surface is a physical change that takes place over long time periods.

   2. Chemical weathering can create <u>cave</u> formations.

   3. Acid rain is a form of <u>unnatural</u> chemical change.

Discussion Question

What is the difference between a physical and a chemical change? In a physical change the identity of the substance remains the same; in a chemical change a new substance is formed.

Electromagnetic Waves (continued)

E. **Ultraviolet radiation** is higher in frequency and has shorter wavelengths than visible light.

   1. Too much exposure to ultraviolet radiation from the Sun can cause sunburn and other health problems.

   2. Since ultraviolet radiation can kill cells, it is sometimes used to <u>sterilize</u> equipment.

   3. The <u>ozone layer</u> in Earth's upper atmosphere helps protect the surface by absorbing much of the Sun's ultraviolet radiation.

F. <u>**X rays**</u> and **gamma rays**, with even higher frequencies than ultraviolet rays, can go right through skin and muscles.

   1. Too much exposure to X rays or gamma rays can damage or kill cells.

   2. X rays are useful in <u>medical diagnosis</u> if used with appropriate precautions.

   3. Gamma rays, which have the highest frequency, can be used to treat <u>cancerous tumors</u> and to kill bacteria in food.

G. Some <u>astronomical</u> objects emit no visible light but are known through <u>infrared</u> and radio images; satellite observations <u>outside</u> Earth's atmosphere help scientists study space at wavelengths that do not reach Earth's surface.

Discussion Question

How can X rays and gamma rays be useful? X rays can be used in medical diagnosis and gamma rays can be used to treat cancer and kill bacteria in food.

END

Motion and Momentum

Underlined words and phrases are to be filled in by students on the Note-taking Worksheet.

Section 1   What is motion?

A. All matter is constantly in <u>motion</u>.

B. Motion involves a <u>change</u> in position.

   1. An object changes position relative to a <u>reference</u> point.

   2. <u>Distance</u> is the total length of the route an object travels when it moves.

   3. <u>Displacement</u> includes distance and direction of the stopping point from the starting point.

C. Distance traveled divided by the time taken to travel the distance is called **speed**.

   1. The formula for <u>speed</u> can be written as: speed = distance/time.

   2. The units of speed are units of distance divided by units of time; in SI units, speed is given as <u>meters per second</u> (m/s).

   3. An object in motion can change <u>speeds</u> many times as it moves from one point to another, speeding up or slowing down.

     a. Average speed is the total distance traveled divided by total time taken.

     b. An object's speed at a particular moment in time is called **instantaneous speed**.

     c. <u>Constant</u> speed occurs when an object travels at a steady rate with the same instantaneous speed for some period of time.

D. Motion can be <u>graphed</u> on a distance-time graph with time plotted on the horizontal axis and distance plotted on the vertical axis.

   1. The steeper the line on a distance-time graph, the greater the <u>speed</u>.

   2. A horizontal line on a distance-time graph indicates that no change in <u>position</u> is occurring, and the speed is <u>zero</u>.

E. <u>Velocity</u>—speed of an object and its direction of motion; velocity changes if either, or both, of these changes.

Discussion Question

What is instantaneous speed? The speed of an object at a particular moment in time

END

Electromagnetic Waves

Underlined words and phrases are to be filled in by students on the Note-taking Worksheet.

Section 2   The Electromagnetic Spectrum

A. Electromagnetic waves have a series of different frequencies and wavelengths called the **electromagnetic spectrum**.

   1. For waves that travel with the same speed, wavelength increases as frequency <u>decreases</u>.

   2. Radiant energy decreases as <u>wavelength</u> increases.

B. <u>**Radio waves**</u> have the lowest frequency and carry the least energy.

   1. AM and FM radio signals and television signals are types of radio waves; they can be sent with radio waves using a transmitting and receiving antenna.

     a. One way to make radio waves is to make electrons vibrate up and down in a piece of metal called an antenna.

     b. The radio waves from the <u>transmitting</u> antenna can cause electrons in another piece of metal, such as a receiving antenna, to move up and down, creating an alternating current.

     c. The <u>current</u> can be used to produce sound from a loudspeaker, allowing for the transmission of music, television shows, and telephone signals.

   2. <u>Microwaves</u> have a higher frequency and shorter wavelength than radio waves; they are used for some phone calls and to heat food.

   3. <u>Radar</u> uses electromagnetic waves to locate objects by measuring the time it takes for the waves to reach the object, be reflected, and return.

C. <u>**Infrared waves**</u> have wavelengths between one thousandth and 0.7 millionths of a meter and feel warm or hot.

   1. Infrared <u>detectors</u> sense objects that are warmer or colder than their environment; TV and VCR remote controls also use infrared waves.

   2. Some animals, such as piranhas and rattlesnakes, can detect infrared waves, which helps them find prey.

D. <u>**Visible light**</u> has wavelengths between 0.7 and 0.4 millionths of a meter.

   1. What you see as different colors are electromagnetic waves of different <u>wavelengths</u>.

   2. Red light has the <u>longest</u> wavelength (lowest frequency); blue light has the <u>shortest</u> wavelength (highest frequency).

TURN

CHAPTER 6

Content Outline for Teaching

Motion and Momentum

Underlined words and phrases are to be filled in by students on the Note-taking Worksheet.

Section 2   Acceleration

A. <u>Acceleration</u>—change in velocity divided by the time for the change to occur; it can include an object's speeding up, slowing down, and/or changing direction

B. Acceleration can be <u>calculated</u> if you know how an object's velocity has changed during a given time period.

1. The formula for calculating <u>acceleration</u> is: acceleration = final speed – initial speed/time or $a = (s_f - s_i)/t$.

   a. The unit of acceleration is distance divided by time squared; in SI units, acceleration is given as <u>meters per second squared</u> (m/s^2).

   b. Acceleration is <u>positive</u> when an object speeds up and <u>negative</u> when an object slows down.

2. Accelerated motion can be <u>graphed</u> with speed on the vertical axis and time on the horizontal axis.

   a. An object that is speeding up will have a line on a speed-time graph that slopes <u>upward</u>.

   b. An object that is slowing down will have a line on a speed-time graph that slopes <u>downward</u>.

   c. A horizontal line would indicate acceleration of <u>zero</u>, or constant speed.

Discussion Question

Acceleration includes what three ways an object's motion can change?
Speeding up, slowing down, or changing direction

END

CHAPTER 13 Content Outline for Teaching

Electromagnetic Waves

Section 1   The Nature of Electromagnetic Waves

A. **Electromagnetic waves**, produced by charged particles in motion, travel through space, transferring energy.

B. An electromagnetic wave is composed of two <u>force</u> fields—an electric field and a magnetic field.

   1. Earth's gravity field exerts a <u>force</u> on all objects and extends out into space.

   2. A <u>magnetic field</u> exerts a force on other magnets, causing them to line up along the direction of the magnetic field.

   3. The <u>electric field</u> surrounding a charged particle exerts a force on all other charged particles in the field.

     a. A <u>moving</u> charged particle is surrounded by an electric field and a magnetic field.

     b. As a charged particle moves up and down, it produces an electromagnetic <u>wave</u>.

C. Electromagnetic waves have a <u>wavelength</u> and a <u>frequency</u>.

   1. One complete vibration of the charged particle up and down creates one <u>wavelength</u> in an electromagnetic wave.

   2. The number of <u>wavelengths</u> that pass by a point in 1 second is the frequency of the electromagnetic wave.

D. **Radiant energy**—energy carried by an electromagnetic wave

   1. The amount of energy carried by an electromagnetic wave is determined by its <u>frequency</u>.

   2. The higher the frequency, the <u>more</u> energy the electromagnetic wave has.

E. Electromagnetic waves travel at the speed of light, <u>300,000</u> km/s, in space.

Discussion Question

What two force fields are found in an electromagnetic wave? an electric field and a magnetic field

END

CHAPTER **6** Content Outline for Teaching — **Motion and Momentum**

Underlined words and phrases are to be filled in by students on the Note-taking Worksheet.

Section 3   Momentum

A. The amount of matter in an object is its **mass**; <u>inertia</u> is the tendency of an object to resist a change in its motion.

B. <u>Momentum</u>—measure of how hard it is to stop an object; calculated as mass times velocity

  1. With <u>momentum</u> expressed as *p*, the equation can be written as: $p = mv$.

  2. Momentum <u>increases</u> if the mass or velocity of the object increases.

  3. Momentum has direction that is the same direction as its velocity.

C. <u>Law of conservation of momentum</u>—the total momentum of objects that collide with each other does not change.

  1. There are <u>many</u> ways collisions can occur.

    a. In one type, objects stick together and <u>move</u> still stuck together, although possibly at different speeds.

    b. In another type, two objects bounce off each other when they collide, and may transfer <u>momentum</u> from one to the other.

  2. In both cases, the <u>total</u> momentum of the objects that collide is the same before and after the collision.

Discussion Question

How is momentum calculated? Momentum equals mass times velocity.

END

G. When two notes that are close in frequency are played together, they combine to form a wave that slowly varies in loudness, this creates a beat with a frequency of the <u>difference</u> in frequencies of the two notes.

H. <u>Reverberation</u>—repeated echoes of sound

I. The human ear has <u>three</u> basic parts.
   1. The outer ear <u>collects</u> sound waves and directs them into the ear canal.
   2. In the middle ear, sound waves vibrate the **eardrum** which passes the vibrations to the hammer, anvil, and stirrup bones, which amplify the sound waves.
   3. The oval window at the inner ear transmits the vibrations through a fluid to cells lining the <u>cochlea</u>; these cells generate nerve impulses carrying information about the sound that travel along the auditory nerve to the brain.

J. The ear can be <u>damaged</u> by disease, age, and exposure to loud noises.

Discussion Question

How does music differ from other sounds? Music is a group of sounds that have been deliberately produced to make a regular pattern

END

Force and Newton's Laws

Section 1 Newton's First Law

A. **Force**—push or pull on an object

   1. The combination of all the forces acting on an object is the **net force.**

   2. When forces are **balanced forces**, they cancel each other out and do not change an object's motion; when forces are **unbalanced forces**, the motion of an object changes.

B. Newton's **first law** of motion—an object will remain at rest or move with constant speed unless a force is applied.

C. **Friction** is a force that resists sliding between two touching surfaces or through air or water.

   1. Friction **slows down** an object's motion.

   2. **Static** friction—the type of friction that prevents an object from moving when a force is applied

   3. **Sliding** friction is due to the microscopic roughness of two surfaces; it slows down a sliding object.

   4. **Rolling** friction between the ground and a wheel allows the wheel to roll.

Discussion Question

What are three types of friction? Static friction, sliding friction, and rolling friction

END

Section 2   Music

A. Music is a group of sounds that have been deliberately produced to make a regular pattern.

   1. Natural frequency—frequency at which a particular object will vibrate

      a. Natural frequency depends on the size and shape of the object and the material it is made from.

      b. Musical instruments use the natural frequencies of strings, drumheads, or columns of air to produce notes.

   2. Resonance occurs when an object is made to vibrate at its natural frequency by absorbing energy from a sound wave or another object vibrating at this frequency.

B. The **fundamental frequency** is the lowest frequency produced by a particular object; **overtones** are higher frequency waves that are multiples of the fundamental frequency.

C. Musical instrument—device that produces a musical sound

D. Stringed instruments produce music by making strings vibrate; a hollow chamber or box, called a resonator, usually amplifies the sound.

E. Percussion instruments are struck to make a sound; a chamber attached to the vibrating surface resonates the sound to amplify it.

F. Brass and woodwind instruments use air columns in pipes of different lengths to produce sound.

   1. Woodwinds change notes by changing the length of the resonating air column.

   2. The musicians playing brass instruments can change pitch pressing valves to change tube length.

CHAPTER 7 Content Outline for Teaching

Force and Newton's Laws

Underlined words and phrases are to be filled in by students on the Note-taking Worksheet.

Section 2   Newton's Second Law

A. Newton's <u>second law</u> of motion connects force, acceleration, and mass; it explains that an object acted upon by a force will accelerate in the direction of the force; acceleration equals net force divided by mass.

B. <u>Gravity</u>—attractive force between two objects; depends on the mass of the objects and distance between them; gravitational force is also called <u>weight</u>.

C. The second law explains how to <u>calculate</u> the acceleration of an object if its mass and the forces acting on it are both known.

D. In circular motion, the <u>centripetal</u> force is always perpendicular to the motion.

E. The **terminal velocity** is reached when the force of gravity is balanced by air resistance; the size of the air resistance force depends on the shape of an object and its speed.

F. An object can speed up, slow down, or turn in the direction of the net force when <u>unbalanced</u> forces act on it.

Discussion Question

The size of air resistance force depends on what two variables? Shape of an object and its speed

END

F. <u>Echo</u>—a sound wave reflected off of a hard surface

    1. The delay in reflection of sound is used to measure <u>distances</u> such as in sonar systems which map the ocean floor and other undersea features.

    2. Some animals use <u>echolocation</u> to navigate and hunt.

G. <u>Doppler effect</u>—change in frequency that is due to the motion of a sound source or listener

H. Sound waves <u>diffract</u>, which means they can bend around obstacles or spread out after passing through a narrow opening.

I. Sound waves can be used in <u>medicine</u> to treat disorders or make an image of the body's interior; ultra-sound uses <u>high</u>-frequency sound as an alternative to some surgeries.

Discussion Question

What is the loudness of a sound? The human perception of how much energy a sound wave carries; louder sounds have greater amplitude.

END

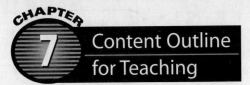

CHAPTER **7** Content Outline for Teaching

Force and Newton's Laws

Underlined words and phrases are to be filled in by students on the Note-taking Worksheet.

Section 3   Newton's Third Law

A. Newton's <u>third law</u> **of motion** states that forces always act in equal but opposite pairs; for every action there is an equal and opposite reaction.

B. Action-reaction forces are always the same size but are in <u>opposite</u> directions and act on different objects.

   1. When the mass of one object is considerably <u>larger</u> than the mass of another object, the action-reaction force is not noticeable.

   2. <u>Air</u> and <u>water</u> exert action-reaction forces with objects such as hands or canoe paddles.

   3. A <u>rocket</u> launches due to the equal but opposite forces of the burning fuel.

Discussion Question

What does Newton's third law of motion state? Forces always act in equal but opposite pairs.

END

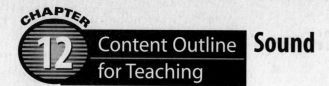

Underlined words and phrases are to be filled in by students on the Note-taking Worksheet.

Section 1   What is sound?

A. Sound is produced by <u>vibrations</u>.

B. A sound wave is a <u>compressional</u> wave in which air molecules move back and forth along the direction the sound wave is moving.

  1. A soundwave is created by a <u>series</u> of compressions and rarefactions.

    a. A <u>compression</u> is a region of higher density air molecules.

    b. A region of lower density air molecules is called a <u>rarefaction</u>.

  2. Sound waves can be described by their <u>wavelength</u> and <u>frequency</u>.

C. Sound waves can travel through various materials at different <u>speeds</u>.

  1. Sound travels <u>fastest</u> through solids, and <u>slowest</u> through gases.

  2. Sound travels faster in a <u>warmer</u> substance.

D. <u>Loudness</u> is the human perception of how much energy a sound wave carries.

  1. Sound waves with greater <u>amplitude</u> carry more energy and sound louder.

  2. The decibel (db) scale describes the energy carried by sound waves.

E. <u>Pitch</u>—how high or low a sound seems

  1. Pitch is related to frequency and wavelength; the <u>higher</u> the frequency and the <u>shorter</u> the wavelength, the <u>higher</u> the pitch.

  2. The length and thickness of <u>vocal cords</u> help determine the pitch of the human voice.

    a. Shorter, thinner chords vibrate at <u>higher</u> frequencies than longer or thicker ones.

    b. People can vary their vocal pitch within a limited range by using the <u>muscles</u> in the throat to stretch the cords.

TURN

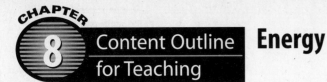

Energy

Underlined words and phrases are to be filled in by students on the Note-taking Worksheet.

Section 1 What is energy?

A. **Energy** is the ability to cause change.

B. Energy from motion is **kinetic** energy.
   1. Kinetic energy increases as an object moves <u>faster</u>.
   2. Kinetic energy increases as the <u>mass</u> of an object increases.

C. Energy stored in an object due to its position is **potential** energy.

D. Energy comes in different <u>forms</u>.
   1. Energy that increases as temperature increases is **thermal** energy.
   2. **Chemical energy**—energy stored in chemical bonds
   3. **Radiant energy**—light energy
   4. Energy from electricity is **electrical** energy.
   5. The nucleus of an atom contains **nuclear** energy.

Discussion Question

How do kinetic energy and potential energy differ? Kinetic energy comes from motion; potential energy is stored energy from an object's position.

END

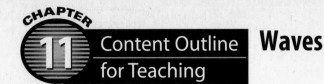

CHAPTER 11 Content Outline for Teaching — **Waves**

Section 3   Wave Behavior

A. <u>Reflection</u>—when a wave strikes an object or surface and bounces off

B. <u>Refraction</u>—when a wave bends and changes speed as it moves from one medium to another

C. <u>Diffraction</u>—the bending of waves around a barrier

D. <u>Interference</u>—two or more waves combine and form a new wave.
   1. <u>Constructive</u> interference—the crest of one wave overlaps the crest of another wave, making a larger wave.
   2. <u>Destructive</u> interference—the crest of one wave overlaps the trough of another wave, making a smaller wave.
   3. If waves with equal amplitude meet crest to trough, they <u>cancel</u> each other out.
   4. Interference can be used in <u>hearing</u> protection.

Discussion Question

How are refraction and diffraction similar and different? Similar—both involve wave bending; different—refraction's bending is caused by a medium change while diffraction's bending is caused by a barrier.

END

Section 2   Energy Transformations

A. Energy is constantly <u>changing</u> from one form to another.

B. Law of <u>**conservation of energy**</u>—energy is never created or destroyed; it merely changes form

C. Energy can be <u>transferred</u> from kinetic to potential energy and back to kinetic.

D. <u>Machines</u> transform energy from one form to another.
   1. Chemical energy can be <u>transferred</u> to kinetic, radiant, thermal, or electrical energy.
   2. <u>Electrical</u> energy can be transformed to kinetic, chemical, electrical, or thermal energy.
   3. Unlike other forms of energy, thermal energy is not easy to <u>store</u>.

E. A **turbine**'s kinetic energy is converted to electrical energy by a <u>**generator**</u> at a power plant.

Discussion Question

What form of energy is the most difficult to store? Thermal energy

END

CHAPTER 11 Content Outline for Teaching

Waves

Section 2   Wave Properties

A. <u>Amplitude</u>—a measure of how high crests are; the greater the amplitude, the more energy a wave carries.

B. <u>Wavelength</u>—distance from the top of one crest to the top of the next crest or from the bottom of one trough to the bottom of the next trough

C. <u>Frequency</u>—number of wavelengths passing a given point per second
   1. Longer wavelengths result in <u>smaller</u> frequencies.
   2. <u>Larger</u> frequencies result in shorter wavelengths.
   3. <u>Color</u> and <u>pitch</u> result from wavelengths and frequencies of light and sound.

D. Wave <u>speed</u>—how fast a wave travels through a medium
   1. Mechanical waves travel faster in a medium in which atoms are <u>closer</u> together.
   2. Electromagnetic waves travel faster in a medium with <u>fewer</u> atoms in it.

Discussion Question
Name four properties of waves. amplitude, wavelength, frequency, and speed

END

CHAPTER 8 Content Outline for Teaching — Energy

Section 3   Sources of Energy

A. Energy comes from either the <u>Sun</u> or from radioactive <u>atoms</u> in the Earth.

B. <u>Fossil fuels</u> include oil, natural gas, and coal.
  1. Fossil fuels contain <u>chemical energy</u> from the Sun's radiant energy via photosynthesis.
  2. **<u>Nonrenewable</u> resources** such as fossil fuels are used up faster than they can be replaced.

C. <u>Nuclear</u> energy comes from the nuclei of uranium atoms.

D. <u>Hydroelectricity</u> from the potential energy of water is a **renewable resource.**

E. **<u>Alternative resources</u>** of energy may be safer for people and the environment.
  1. <u>Solar</u> energy can be captured in thermal collectors or **photovoltaic** collectors.
  2. <u>Geothermal</u> energy—thermal energy contained in hot magma
  3. <u>Windmills</u> can generate electricity without polluting the environment.

F. <u>Conserving</u> energy will help prevent energy shortages and allow fossil fuels to last longer.

Discussion Question

Why is it important to conserve energy? To prevent energy shortages and to stretch fossil fuel supplies

END

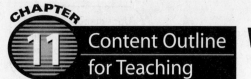

CHAPTER 11 Content Outline for Teaching   Waves

Section 1   What are waves?

A. Rhythmic disturbances that carry energy without carrying matter are called **waves.**

B. Molecules <u>transport</u> wave energy without themselves moving, like a line of people passing a ball.

C. <u>Mechanical</u> **waves** use matter to transfer energy.

    1. <u>Transverse</u> **wave**—wave energy causes matter in the medium to move up and down or back and forth at right angles to the wave.

    2. <u>**Compressional wave**</u>—matter in the medium moves forward and backward in same direction as the wave.

D. <u>Sound</u> waves—compressional waves caused by colliding air molecules

E. <u>Electromagnetic</u> **waves**—transfer energy without using matter; produced by electrically charged particles

Discussion Question

What is the difference between a mechanical wave and an electromagnetic wave? Mechanical waves use matter to transfer energy; electromagnetic waves use electrically charged particles to carry energy.

END

Work and Simple Machines

Underlined words and phrases are to be filled in by students on the Note-taking Worksheet.

Section 1   Work and Power

A. <u>Work</u>—occurs when a force causes an object to move in the same direction that the force is applied

1. Work involves <u>motion</u>, not just effort.

2. Work is done only when the <u>force</u> you exert on an object is in the same direction as the object's motion; lifting a clothes basket is work, but carrying it while walking is not work.

3. When a force is exerted at an angle, only the part of the force that is in the <u>same</u> direction as the motion does work.

B. Work can be calculated using the formula *work = <u>force</u> × distance*.

1. Force is measured in newtons, distance is measured in meters, and the unit for work is the <u>joule</u>.

2. Distance in the work equation is the distance an object moves only <u>while</u> the force is being applied.

C. <u>Power</u>—how quickly work is done

1. Power can be calculated using the formula *power = <u>work done</u> / time needed*.

2. The unit of power is the <u>watt</u>.

3. Doing work on an object increases the object's kinetic and potential <u>energy</u>.

4. The amount of work done is the amount of energy <u>transferred</u> and can be expressed in the power formula in place of work done: *power = energy transferred / time needed*.

5. Power is always the <u>rate</u> at which energy is transferred.

Discussion Question

Is carrying a book while walking work? Why or why not? No, because the book's motion is not in the same direction as the force applied to it.

END

CHAPTER

10 Content Outline for Teaching

Thermal Energy

Underlined words and phrases are to be filled in by students on the Note-taking Worksheet.

Section 3 Engines and Refrigerators

A. <u>Engine</u>—device that converts thermal energy into mechanical energy

1. In an <u>external combustion engine</u>, such as a steam engine, the fuel is burned outside the engine to produce thermal energy.

2. In an **internal combustion engine**, fuel burns in a combustion chamber inside the engine.

3. Most cars have a four-stroke engine with four or more <u>combustion chambers</u>, or cylinders.

   a. Each cylinder contains a <u>piston</u> that can move up and down.

   b. A mixture of <u>fuel and air</u> is injected into the cylinder and ignited with a spark, which pushing the piston down.

   c. This up-and-down-motion of pistons turns a rod called a <u>crankshaft</u>, which turns the wheels of the car.

4. Other types of internal combustion engines include <u>diesel</u> engines, which use high pressure instead of a spark for ignition, and two-stroke gasoline engines, commonly used in <u>lawn mowers</u>.

B. A <u>refrigerator</u> absorbs heat from food and materials inside the refrigerator and transfers it to the surrounding air.

1. A <u>liquid coolant</u> is changed into a cold gas that absorbs heat from the inside of the refrigerator.

2. A compressor compresses the <u>coolant gas</u>, making it warmer than room temperature.

3. The coolant gas <u>transfers</u> heat to the room, then changes back into a coolant liquid, and the cycle is repeated.

4. An <u>air conditioner</u> works much like a refrigerator to cool a house.

5. A <u>heat pump</u> can be used for cooling and heating a house by reversing itself based on outside temperature.

Discussion Question

How does an internal combustion engine differ from an external combustion engine? An internal combustion engine burns fuel in a combustion chamber inside the engine, while an external combustion engine uses thermal energy from fuel burned outside the engine.

END

Work and Simple Machines

Underlined words and phrases are to be filled in by students on the Note-taking Worksheet.

Section 2   Using Machines

A. <u>Machine</u> —device that makes doing work easier

B. Machines change the <u>way</u> a person does work, not the amount of work that needs to be done.

1. <u>**Input force**</u>—the effort, or work, force you exert on a machine

2. <u>**Output force**</u>—the resistance force, or the work a machine does to move an object over some distance

3. When using a machine, the output work can never be <u>greater</u> then the input work.

4. <u>**Mechanical advantage**</u>—number of times the input force is multiplied by a machine; calculated as *mechanical advantage = output force / input force*

   a. Some machines make work easier by allowing you to exert a smaller force over a <u>longer</u> distance, resulting in a mechanical advantage of more than one.

   b. Other machines allow you to exert your force over a <u>shorter</u> distance resulting in a mechanical advantage of less than one.

   c. Still other machines allow you to change the <u>direction</u> of input force resulting in a mechanical advantage equal to one.

C. <u>Efficiency</u>—ability of a machine to convert input work to output work; calculated as *efficiency = output work / input work × 100%*

1. <u>Friction</u> reduces efficiency by converting some work into heat.

2. The efficiency of a real machine is always <u>less than</u> 100 percent because of friction.

3. Oil, or another lubricant, can increase efficiency by reducing the number of <u>contact</u> <u>points</u> between surfaces.

Discussion Question

What is the efficiency of a machine and how can it be improved? Efficiency is the ability of a machine to convert input work to output work. It can be improved by using a lubricant to reduce friction.

END

E. <u>Thermal pollution</u>, caused by adding warmer water to a body of water.

   1. Thermal pollution can kill fish and other aquatic organisms due to a reduction in <u>oxygen</u> in warmer water.

   2. Thermal pollution can be reduced by <u>cooling</u> water from factories, power plants, and runoff before it is released into a body of water.

Discussion Question

How do conductors differ from insulators? Conductors are often metals that transfer heat readily; insulators are often gases or liquids that do not transfer heat easily.

END

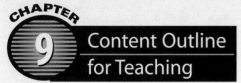

CHAPTER 9 **Content Outline for Teaching**

Work and Simple Machines

Underlined words and phrases are to be filled in by students on the Note-taking Worksheet.

Section 3   Simple Machines

A. <u>Simple machine</u>—does work with only one movement; a machine made of a combination of simple machines is a **compound machine**.

B. <u>Inclined plane</u>—a flat, sloped surface

1. Less <u>force</u> is needed to move an object from one height to another using an inclined plan than is needed to lift the object.

2. As the inclined plane gets longer, the force needed to move the object gets <u>smaller</u>.

3. The <u>mechanical advantage</u> of an inclined plane is the length of the inclined plane divided by its height.

4. Inclined plane that moves—**wedge**; changes the direction of the applied force; example: your front teeth

5. <u>Screw</u>—Inclined plane wrapped around a cylinder or post; the screw threads form the inclined plane on a screw; the mechanical advantage of the screw is the length of the inclined plane wrapped around the screw divided by the length of the screw.

C. <u>Lever</u>—any rigid rod or plank that pivots about a point.

1. the point about which the lever pivots—<u>fulcrum</u>

2. Mechanical advantage—divide the distance from the fulcrum to the <u>input</u> force by the distance from the fulcrum to the <u>output</u> force.

3. Levers can be divided into classes depending on the position of the <u>fulcrum</u>.

D. <u>Wheel and axle</u>—two circular objects of different sizes that rotate together

1. The mechanical advantage of a wheel and axle is found by <u>dividing</u> the radius of the wheel by the radius of the axle.

2. In some cases, the input force turns the wheel, and the axle exerts the output force, resulting in a mechanical advantage <u>greater</u> than one; examples are a doorknob, a steering wheel, and a screwdriver.

3. In other cases, the input force turns the axle, and the wheel exerts the output force, resulting in a mechanical advantage of <u>less</u> than one; examples are a fan and a ferris wheel.

TURN

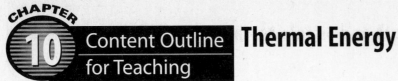

Thermal Energy

Section 2   Heat

A. <u>Heat</u>—thermal energy that is transferred from one object to another when the objects are at different temperatures

    1. Thermal energy always moves from <u>warmer</u> to <u>cooler</u> objects.

    2. The transfer of heat by direct contact between the particles of substances is called **conduction**; conduction occurs most easily in solids, where molecules are close together.

    3. Heat transfer by **radiation** occurs when electromagnetic waves carry energy through space or matter.

    4. **Convection** describes the transfer of thermal energy by the movement of molecules from one part (warmer) of a material to another (cooler) part.

        a. Convection occurs <u>naturally</u> as a hot gas or liquid moves from one place to another; wind is caused by convection in air; rising warmer air forms a convection cycle with falling cooler air.

        b. Convection can be <u>forced</u> as when a fan blows cooler air over warmer air produced by a machine.

B. **Conductors** are materials that transfer heat readily; metals such as copper and gold are the best heat conductors.

C. An <u>insulator</u> is a material that does not transfer heat easily; liquids and gases are usually better insulators than solids.

D. Objects absorb heat at different <u>rates</u> depending on what materials they are made of.

    1. **Specific heat**—amount of heat needed to raise the temperature of 1 kg of a substance by 1° C

    2. More heat is needed to change the temperature of a material with a <u>high</u> specific heat (such as water) than one with a <u>low</u> specific heat (such as sand).

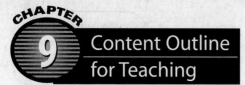

E. <u>Pulley</u>—grooved wheel with a rope or chain wrapped around it

1. <u>Fixed</u> pulleys, such as on window blinds or flagpoles, are attached to an overhead structure and change the direction of the force you exert; they have a mechanical advantage of one.

2. <u>Moveable</u> pulleys are attached to the object being lifted and allow you to exert a smaller force; they have a mechanical advantage of two.

3. Pulley <u>system</u>—combination of fixed and movable pulleys

Discussion Question

What is the difference between a simple machine and a compound machine? A simple machine makes only one movement; a compound machine is made up of multiple simple machines and makes more than one

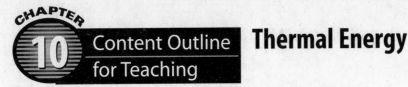

Section 1   Temperature and Thermal Energy

A. <u>Temperature</u>—measure of the average value of the kinetic energy of the molecules in a substance; the higher the temperature, the faster the molecules are moving.

1. Objects tend to <u>expand</u> with increased temperature because their molecules speed up and move farther apart; objects tend to contract when they are cooled.

   a. The amount of expansion or contraction depends on the <u>material</u> and the amount of change in <u>temperature</u>.

   b. Liquids usually expand <u>more</u> than solids.

2. Temperature is commonly measured using a <u>thermometer</u>.

3. Thermometers need numbers on a <u>scale</u> to give a temperature reading.

   a. The <u>Fahrenheit</u> scale gives water a freezing temperature of 32°F and a boiling temperature of 212°F.

   b. The <u>Celsius</u> scale gives water a freezing temperature of 0° C and a boiling temperature of 100°C.

   c. The formula to convert temperature from °F to °C is $°C = (5/9)(°F - 32)$.

   d. The <u>Kelvin</u> scale gives the temperature 0° K to the lowest temperature an object can have, a temperature known as absolute zero; $°C = K - 273$.

B. An object's **thermal energy** is the sum of the kinetic and potential energy of all the molecules in the object.

1. Potential energy is energy that can be <u>converted</u> into kinetic energy. Potential energy <u>changes</u> as molecules move closer together or farther apart.

2. Temperature and thermal energy are different concepts; <u>thermal energy</u> is related to the quantity of molecules.

Discussion Question

What are three scales that can be used to measure temperature? Fahrenheit, Celsius, and Kelvin

END